MONKEY TALES

Told and Adapted by Ernest Lloyd

Editorial Department

"Our Little Friend"

Grateful acknowledgment is made to Mr. Elwyn
R. Sanborn of the New York Zoölogical Society,
to the owners of the Los Angeles Monkey Farm,
and to the Milwaukee, Wisconsin, Zoo, for many
of the pictures used in this little book.

ISBN: 0-8163-2120-5

PACIFIC PRESS PUBLISHING ASSOCIATION
Nampa, Idaho
Oshawa, Ontario, Canada

The monkey's life is glad and free;
He swings with grace from tree to tree;
His arms and legs have even length;
In all his limbs he has much strength.
He is more gay and more care free;
But who would e'er a monkey be?

The Monkey That Was Rescued

HEY, mister," shouted Tommy Burton, "you've lost your monkey!" Tommy had run a long way after the circus with the baby monkey that he'd found beside the road, and now was almost breathless.

"I didn't lose him," shouted the circus man. "The monk's dying, so I threw him out."

Tommy could scarcely believe his ears. Threw a poor little monkey out because he was dying!

"Can't you nurse him better?" he shouted indignantly.

"Naw, that monk's no good. He'll die before night. No use keeping him."

Mingled anger and pity filled Tommy's eyes.

"Well, sir, you'll be sorry some day that you treated him like that!" And he turned and walked toward home, with the monkey cradled in his arm. The dusty road felt hot and painful to Tommy's bare feet, so when he came to a lake he was glad to sit on the bank and dangle his feet in the water. Then he gave the monkey a drink.

"Well, Monk," he said, "that circus man may think he knows a lot, but I'm going to do my best to show him that he doesn't know a live monkey when he sees one! I don't know much about doctoring people, but mother knows an awful lot." So, after bathing the monkey's head with cool water, he nestled him carefully in his blouse, and hurried home.

When Tommy arrived, tired and hungry, the monkey was still alive and seemed a little brighter than when Tommy had found him.

"Seems to me that all he needs is good food and peace and quiet," remarked his mother, when she saw the invalid. "I guess the poor little thing's just tired of all the noise and bustle of the circus. I'll cook him some gruel; you make him a bed of clean straw, and put some fresh water near; and then we must leave him strictly alone. We've done all we can for him; we'll have to let nature do the rest."

It was hard for the boy not to stay and caress his new friend; but in the morning he got up with the dawn, and ran to the shed to see how the monkey was getting along He hesitated to open the door, for fear of what he might find. Imagine his surprise when, peeping cautiously around the door, he found the little fellow perched on a beam above his head!

Tommy's joy was so great that he clapped his hands, and the monkey went chattering away to the farthest corner.

"There," thought Tommy regretfully, "the first thing I do is to scare him! I guess I don't deserve to have a monkey!"

But they were soon friends again, and Tommy ran to tell his mother the good news.

Monkey was not well by any means; and Tommy and his mother had to nurse him carefully for a whole week before he was cured. Then Tommy was the proudest boy in the whole world, for the monkey, which he now called Peter, followed him everywhere like a dog, and became so intelligent that he seemed to understand everything Tommy said.

"Well, mother," said Tommy, "I can hardly believe that I've got a real live monkey that won't run away from me or anything! Do you remember how I always dreamed of one? But I never, never thought I'd get one of my very own!"

Mother looked very serious. "Have you ever thought, Tommy, of what will happen when the circus returns?"

Tommy's eyes opened wide. "Aw, mom, you don't mean that Peter'll leave me and go back to the circus, do you?"

"No, dear; but the man didn't give you the monkey, you know."

"But he threw him away!" exclaimed Tommy indignantly. "And I reckon I've got a right to Peter when I saved his life."

"Think it over, Tommy, think it over."

Tommy thought it over a lot, and finally decided he'd have to give Peter back to his owner.

But there might be one way out of the difficulty; and with this in mind Tommy started saving his pennies, and doing all kinds of odd jobs to earn more. Perhaps he could buy Pete if he had the price.

Tommy never knew a year to go so quickly; and as circus week drew near, he grew more and more fearful. He couldn't bear the thought of parting with his friend, especially as he had taught him so many cunning tricks.

Tears filled Tommy's eyes as he walked toward the circus field, with Peter perched on his shoulder. "When he sees how cunning you are, Pete, he's sure to want you!"

Pete didn't quite understand the tears, but chattered excitedly over the unaccustomed trip to the village.

"Yes, my boy," said the circus master, when he heard Tommy's story. "I heard about the man who threw the monkey out, and I fired him. We don't allow such things to happen if we can help it.

"So this is the sick baby, is it? Well, well! I'll say you're a clever boy to nurse him back to life. What are you going to do with him now?"

"He's yours, sir," said Tommy in a choked voice. "But—but he's an awful cute monkey, an'—an' you'll have to be kind to him."

There was a big lump in Tommy's throat, and he did not seem to be able to say the words he'd been rehearsing so long.

"Can he do any tricks?"

Instantly his pride in the monkey's accomplishments overcame every other feeling, and Tommy put his friend through all his funny tricks.

"Say, he's some monkey!" exclaimed the showman. "How much do you want for him?"

Tommy gasped. "Want for him?"

"Sure. You've trained him so well that I'll buy him for whatever you ask."

After a breathless pause, Tommy's words tumbled over one another in his excitement. "Oh, sir, if—if you think he's mine, just let me keep him—that's all I want! You see, sir, he—he's my pal, an'—an' I couldn't sell my pal! I don't want money—all I want is Peter!" And he hid his face in Peter's coat.

The great man's arm went around Tommy's shoulders. "You're right, boy; there's no money in the world that can buy a pal. Keep him. And bring him in to see his mother and the rest of the circus every day if you like. No, you don't pay to get in. You and Peter are my guests for the week!"

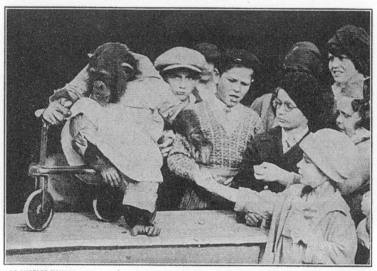

Getting acquainted with a young chimpanzee at the Monkey Farm. He is very fond of his kiddie kar.

A Sleepy Monkey

LITTLE monkeys get hungry and tired and sleepy, just as children do. Here is a story of one that lives in Buffalo, New York. He belongs to an organ grinder, who stopped in front of a veranda where a kind-hearted gentleman sat. When he came up and held out his little cap for a bit of money, the gentleman, who is very fond of animals, gave him a red-cheeked apple. The monkey jumped up on his lap and ate the apple, and between bites he fixed his bright eyes on the face of his new friend. He must have made up his mind that he could trust him, for, as he finished the apple, he laid his head against the gentleman's arm and fell asleep. The kind friend of animals paid the organ grinder to play a long time, so that the tired little monkey could have his nap. When he awoke, his master pulled the chain, and he followed the organ again, much brighter and happier for the kindness shown to him.

Java Mother and Baby.

Los Angeles Monkey Farm

Monkey mothers are very watchful of their little ones, and guard them constantly.

The Monkey and the Gobbler

A SEA captain, who lived in Washington during his stays on land, was very fond of fowls of all sorts, and especially prized an old gobbler that had been long in his possession.

Returning from a voyage, he brought home a mischievous young monkey, which easily succeeded in making considerable trouble for his master.

One day, hearing a terrible commotion in the hennery, the captain entered and found Jocko, the monkey, with the gobbler under his arm, deliberately pulling out the poor bird's last beautiful tail feather. The captain rescued the big turkey and punished the monkey, which knew very well why he was chastised.

The next day, again hearing a commotion among the feathered tribe, the captain went to the scene of action. There sat Jocko, with the gobbler between his knees, trying to put the feathers back! The monkey's intentions were now good, but the big turkey seemed quite unable to appreciate them.

Enjoying a little music at the zoo. This picture shows the chimpanzee orchestra at its daily practice. Mary is the first violin and leader, and occupies the center chair. Mike plays the guitar, and does a little "singing", Bill is very fond of his mandolin. How would you like to hear this jungle orchestra?

The Monkeys of India

IN ONE of the small country towns of Northern India where our missionaries located a mission station some years ago lived a large number of small brown monkeys. In fact, in that country there are monkeys in all the towns and villages, and the Hindu people build temples to them and worship them, priests being employed to keep the temples and to feed such of the monkeys as come about the temple from day to day. Of course the monkeys soon learn that food will be found at the temples, and they make their homes in the trees near by.

Throughout India wandering tribes of monkeys raid the fruit trees, scamper about the streets, steal from the grain, vegetable, and sweetmeat shops in the bazaar, and make themselves a general nuisance to the community. Yet, because the Hindu people regard them with reverence, all this is endured under protest because of the loss, but without serious damage to the monkeys, and the animals continue to make their homes in and about the town and village areas.

In the outskirts of the town previously mentioned was an open lot, near the dry bed of a creek. On the creek side of the lot grew a long line of bamboo clumps and also a few large trees. In these trees and clumps of bamboo lived a large tribe of the common brown monkeys; and in the open lot from day to day played the children of the tribe.

One evening friends asked me to go with them to visit this spot, to see the young monkeys at their play. As we sat quietly at one side of the lot, in the midst of which were several medium-sized trees, we saw some twenty or thirty youngsters of the tribe playing what was apparently a game of tag. Up the trunk of a tree would scamper one small monkey, with another hot at his heels. Out on a limb as far as possible he would go, only to drop off to the ground as it dipped with his weight. Then he would rush to another tree or up the same one, continuing until caught, when the process would be reversed. Others were playing at the same game. Those too small for such vigorous play were chasing one another about the ground; while still others were mere onlookers at their more active and speedy brothers and sisters.

At last it began to grow dark, and from the clumps of bamboos and from the trees, fathers and mothers came to call their children to bed. Monkeys, even the children, learn to sleep on the limbs of trees or where the limbs fork out one from another. Here they sit huddled down, and sleep until the first light of dawn awakes them to go foraging in the fields and trees for food.

When, on this night, the fathers and mothers called the little folks, some, like human little folks, were anxious to play, and so held back; but the parents, as good parents should, insisted on obedience, and some young monkeys went scurrying home to bed that night with a sound slap, to remind them that they must obey father and mother and go to bed when called. Inside of five minutes from the first call every little monkey was quiet and on the road to slumberland.

NEW YORK ZOO   White-throated capuchin monkeys from South America

The Monkeys That Wear Boots

THE hunters of Brazil know how monkeys love to imitate, so they take advantage of this curious habit to catch them. They have many little boots made, about large enough to fit a monkey's foot, and they fill the bottom of each boot with soft pitch. Provided with these, they go into the woods where the merry monkeys have their headquarters. These hunters know that they might as well try to catch a bird on the wing as to lay hands on one of these active creatures, so they sit down under the trees where all the monkeys can see them, and stand the little boots along in a row.

The monkeys quickly gather overhead to watch what the men are doing. Then the hunters pull off their own boots, and stand them beside the little boots. After letting the boots remain there a while, they take them up, and, having carefully looked at them,—while the monkeys in the trees are watching every proceeding,—they slowly draw their own boots upon their feet, and hurry away into the thicket, where they can not be seen, leaving the little boots standing in rows under the trees.

As soon as the hunters are out of sight, down come the monkeys. They look sharply at the little boots, then take them up and feel them, smell them, and eye them over and over again. Finally they sit down, as the hunters did, to draw them on their feet. As soon as the boots are fairly on, the hunters rush out from their hiding place. The monkeys take to the trees, but they find they can not climb. They try to pull off the boots, as the men did, but they are stuck fast to their feet. They thus fall easy captives to the cunning hunters, who bear them off in triumph. It will pay us all to be very careful what and whom we imitate.

Jim Pansy with his camera, taking a picture of his friend on the hobby horse.

Joycie Cott, with her pet, whose name is Monty. This little girl is the daughter of Missionary Cott and his wife, who are working among the Davis Indians

A Monkey Hero

MANY years ago a gentleman in England had a fine monkey, a large orang-utan, which, you know, is a large monkey when fully grown. This monkey was very much attached to his master and to the baby boy of the household, who was the pet of the whole family.

One day a fire suddenly broke out in the house, and everybody was running here and there to put it out, while the baby boy in the nursery was almost forgotten in the excitement. When they thought of him, the stairway to his room was all in flames. What could be done?

As they were looking up and wondering, a large hairy hand and arm opened the window, and presently the monkey appeared with the baby in his arms, and carefully climbed down over the porch and brought the child safely to the ground. Nobody else could have done it, for a man can not climb as a monkey can, and is not nearly so strong.

You may imagine how the faithful monkey was praised and petted after that. This is a true story, and the child who was saved was the young Marquis of Kildare.

NEW YORK ZOO

Just a yawn!

Monkey house and grounds at the Milwaukee, Wisconsin, Zoo. Look closely and you can see the monkeys on the trees and on the rope bridge, hanging high in the air.

The Monkeys That Stole the Baby

IN A small town in the southern part of Africa, we are told by the author of "All Sorts," lived a poor man and his wife. Their one child was a great comfort and joy to them. While the father was away at work during the day, the baby boy was carefully watched by the loving mother, for close by the little village were dense woods, where many wild animals lived.

One day the mother rocked her baby to sleep; then, putting him on the bed, she started for the market, to get some needed provisions. Of course she hurried, for the baby was home alone. When she returned with her basket, the baby was not on the bed. Thinking he had rolled off and crept away, she called and looked, but the baby could not be found. Even his little bathtub and sponge and some of his clothes were gone.

When the father came home that night, he found his wife almost wild with grief. Two or three days passed, but all search proved vain, until one morning, the father, while passing through the edge of the forest, saw several monkeys sitting near some rocks. He looked more closely, and saw one monkey holding in her arms—not a monkey—but his baby! Near the monkey stood the little bathtub, and Mrs. Monkey was giving the baby his morning bath. These monkeys had, at some time or other, seen the baby's mother give him his daily bath; so, of course, they wanted to do as she had done. Monkeys are great imitators, you know.

The excited father hastened back to town; and, getting a company of men to go with him, returned to the woods to get his baby. The monkeys were quite angry at first, but finally they dropped the baby on the ground, and hurried away.

NEW YORK ZOO

Some monkeys have no tails, and others have long tails. In South America are the spider monkeys. They have long legs and arms, and a tail that acts like an arm and hand.

The Monkey That Tried to Preach

A PREACHER once brought up an orang-utan, which became so fond of him that wherever he went the monkey always wanted to follow. Before going to a church service, it was always necessary for the preacher to shut the monkey up in his room.

Once, however, the animal escaped from the room and, unseen, followed his master to the church. Carefully and silently the monkey crept in, and then climbed to the top of the old-fashioned sounding board that extended above and partly over the pulpit. There he lay very still until the sermon began.

He then crept to the edge of the sounding board and, overlooking the preacher, imitated all his gestures in so funny a manner that the whole congregation were made to laugh.

The preacher, surprised and disturbed at this ill-timed levity, rebuked his audience for their lack of seriousness. But his reproof failed to change their attitude; the congregation still laughed, and the preacher redoubled his earnestness and his gestures. These the monkey imitated so exactly that the congregation could no longer restrain themselves, but burst out into hearty and continuous laughter.

A special friend of the preacher's then stepped up to him, and pointed out the cause of this improper conduct. The preacher found it a difficult matter to keep from laughing himself. He requested the deacons of the church to take the monkey away, and then he went on with his sermon.

NEW YORK ZOO

A mandrill from West Africa, which belongs to the baboon family, and has strong teeth like a dog, but as sharp as daggers. His cheeks are deeply ribbed, as you see in the picture. They are blue, and his nose is fiery red.

The Polite Monkey

THE monkey certainly teaches us a lesson of making it pleasant for our friends. A naturalist tells a curious story of a gentleman in London who occupied a large home with ample grounds. He bought a lively monkey, which had been nicely trained, and brought him home, dressed up in a hat, coat, and trousers.

A terrier dog belonging to the place saw the monkey sitting on the terrace on the lawn, and started for him. When he got within a few feet, the monkey sat so still and unconcerned that the dog was frightened. He also sat down, and for a minute or two the dog and the monkey glared at each other. The little dog was thinking of renewing the attack, when suddenly the monkey lifted his hat and bowed politely to him. This was too much for the dog; he took refuge under the porch of the house. As soon as the dog was gone, the monkey ran up a tree.

Have no fear! That youngster on the monkey's back is enjoying the ride; and the big
fellow is very fond of carrying him around in this fashion.

The De Brazza monkey,—a rare monkey; one seldom seen in captivity

The Monkey Nurse

THERE is something very kind and tender about the monkey, notwithstanding his love for mischief. There is an interesting story of a monkey that made himself very much beloved on a vessel. He was petted a great deal by the sailors, and did not seem to have those bad traits that some monkeys have. His name was Jocko. The sailors never treated him roughly, and he repaid them with love in return.

On the ship was a spaniel with her four young puppies. At first she did not like Jocko at all, and would not let him come near the place where she and her young ones were kept. She would show so much anger that Jocko would keep away, and go to his friends, the sailors.

But Jocko had as much desire to see and pet the little pups as some small girls have to play with them. One day when the mother spaniel was not present, Jocko went down to the place where the pups were all cuddled together. Then taking them up in his arms, he held them and petted them just as if they were his own children.

While Jocko was thus entertaining the pups, the mother dog came along, and to her great surprise saw her children in the arms of the "nurse." Instead of being angry, she was so much pleased that from that day she treated Jocko with great fondness. Often she would leave him to take care of her pups while she went off to walk around the ship.

This true story shows how even among the lower animals love.will win love.

This is a picture of Nellie, the chimpanzee that enjoys roller skating as much as any girl in the country.

A Japanese monkey and her baby. The little fellow is not allowed to stray from its mother for one instant. It can play within a few feet of her, but a watchful gaze is always turned in its direction.

The Monkey and the Red Caps

A MAN who had a small business in the old city of Cadiz decided to change his residence and move to northern Africa. Before leaving Cadiz, he invested some money in the purchase of those red caps (fezzes) used by so many men in Turkey and northern Africa. Soon after his arrival in Africa, he set out alone to sell his caps in the interior country. Long before sunrise he was off, and reached a shady wood before the heat became too great for traveling. In hot countries the middle of the day is usually set aside for sleep.

The man opened his big bag of red caps, put on one of them, and stretched himself under a tree, and slept until sunset. Imagine his surprise on waking to find the branches of the tree under which he had slept covered

with monkeys with red caps on their heads! They had
seen the man put on his, and as soon as he was asleep had
one and all imitated his example. The poor man was in
a great rage, and, stamping his foot with vexation, threw
his red cap on the ground. Immediately all the monkeys
did the same with theirs! With a very joyful heart the
man quickly gathered up the caps and went on his way.

HERBERT PHOTO

Mr. Five-Hands

MR. FIVE-HANDS is a little ring-tailed monkey that lives at the zoo, where he is a great favorite with the children, because he is so happy-hearted and merry. His cage is his playground, and there he entertains by the hour the crowds who gather to watch his antics and to laugh at his funny, quaint, old-mannish face and his jolly ways.

All Mr. Five-Hands' family lived in the jungle. Indeed, he lived there himself till he was two years old, and played and chattered among the trees with the other monkeys, leaping from bough to bough and mocking the tiger cat and the boa, which were unable to follow him.

There's little in the way of climbing that Mr. Five-Hands can't do, though he isn't a very good walker. And it's that fifth "hand" of his that makes him such a wonderful climber. It helps him to keep his balance, and he can hang by it from a limb and swing back and forth with all the ease imaginable. Of course you have guessed that this "hand" is nothing more nor less than Mr. Five-Hands' long tail. It winds about a bough like a supple finger, and is so muscular that it bears his weight with ease.

Mr. Five-Hands loves to be petted, and he cuddles in the arms of his keeper like a child. He has a plaintive little way of chattering, but, when he take a notion to shriek, it's time to put your fingers in your ears. He is very quick to learn, and his keeper has taught him a number of tricks and trained him to have nice monkey manners—all but table manners. Mr. Five-Hands' way of dining is something to view with pain and sorrow. He is nothing short of a glutton, and wastes three times as much as he eats. He is very fond of boiled rice and milk, bread and milk, potatoes, apples, carrots, and onions too.

Mr. Five-Hands is clean and well coated, and has, apparently, a great dislike for untidiness in others; and, when he is not playing, his favorite diversion is picking specks of sawdust, dirt, fleas, and lice from the coat of his cage mate.

The hanuman monkey, from India,—shy and delicate

A Famous Chimpanzee

MR. ALFRED H. MILES, a popular writer of animal anecdotes, tells this story of a famous chimpanzee, named Charlemagne, that lived in the French town of Grenoble:

For nine years the chimpanzee, which was brought to Grenoble by an African explorer, had enjoyed the freedom of the town. He was allowed to enter almost every house and to help himself to anything he fancied in the fruit and vegetable shops.

The chief reason of the town's great regard for this chimpanzee was that he had rescued a child from drowning in a well. Charlemagne had seen everything, and for him to swing himself over the top of the well was the work of but a moment. He descended rapidly on the rope used for the buckets, grasped the child, and brought her up quickly to her friends.

Charlemagne increased his popularity by spending hours in the children's hospital of the town, playing in the different wards and amusing the children, who were all very fond of him. A bronze statue of this famous monkey now stands in the little town of Grenoble.

They must be very good friends!

Dinner time at the monkey house

The Sad End of a Teasing Monkey

IN AN account of his tour in Siam, Mr. Frederick Seymour, the explorer and naturalist who accompanied Stanley in the search for David Livingstone, says the rivers all through the little kingdom of Siam abound with crocodiles. And the crocodiles are tantalized daily by the monkeys, which annoy them in various ways.

"One day," wrote Mr. Seymour, "I was witness to the monkey's love for teasing and the penalty sometimes paid. A large number of the agile little fellows had gathered in a tree under which a crocodile was sunning himself in some shallow water. One after another the monkeys dropped to the lower branches but were always careful not to approach too near the open jaws of the crocodile; and there they were, yelling at every effort he made to catch a stray leg or arm between his awful teeth.

"The odd sport went on for a full hour, the monkeys growing more and more excited and the crocodile never once losing his patience, probably well aware, from experience, that in the end he would be repaid for having so kindly lent himself to their amusement.

"At last an unlucky monkey slid down the trunk of the tree, passing unceremoniously over the heads and backs of his companions, evidently with the intention of taking the place of the one that occupied the post of danger near the water.

A monkey from Africa was cared for and taught by a family in London. He became very neat in his habits. His table manners were excellent; he never snatched any food, ate slowly, and drank carefully. He could handle the water faucet like a person. He enjoyed standing on the rail of his bed and jumping on the springs, heels over head, like some boys we have met.

The solemn-faced Guereza monkey is sometimes seen in Africa.

"The whole crowd of monkeys yelled and chattered louder than ever, and the crocodile's mouth opened wider, but he gave no other sign of eagerness. The monkey had nearly reached the bottom of the line when he made a misstep, lost his hold, and fell into the awful maw of the crocodile. There was one cry of agony, and the unhappy wight was dragged under the water. The crocodile and his 'lunch' quickly disappeared. The monkeys ran up the tree in terrible haste, their merriment changed to doleful cries; and there they sat wringing their hands and bewailing the sad fate of their companion."

So the poor fellow came to a bad end through the cultivation of a bad habit. There are some other "animals" that possess the love of seeing how near they can get to danger without being hurt. But wise boys and girls curb such desires, and thus avoid what might result disastrously.

GORILLAS

The gorilla lives in the jungles of Africa. It is so large and fierce that no full-grown one has ever been caught alive. It lives upon fruit, and builds a covered platform in a tree for its home. With one stroke of its great arm, it can kill a man or a horse. About the only time, however, that a gorilla will attack a person is in defense of its young. The animal is then extremely dangerous.

Gorillas are very cunning. They have their sentries out during the daytime. These sentries are relieved at regular times with clocklike regularity; and travelers have seen large bowlders worn as smooth as glass from the continual tread of these sentries on the same bowlder.

The Jealous Monkey

A TRAVELING menagerie was showing a large number of monkeys. These little monkeys exercised all their cleverness to share in the cakes and other nice things that their great friend, the elephant, was receiving. One very lively monkey used to get a large portion of the various bits of food offered by the spectators.

One day he failed to obtain the usual attention, and he saw with great indignation that the visitors had transferred their attentions to the next cage. He was very curious to know the cause of this, and at length he managed to poke out a knot in the wood that divided the cages. On peeping through the knot hole, he saw that his monkey neighbor had recently been blessed with a baby monkey. From that moment the big monkey vowed vengeance against the unsuspecting little one. He watched it through the knot hole, he put his hand in and tried to pinch it, and, in fact, he spent his time devising how he might annoy it.

The mother monkey saw the evil designs of her neighbor, and carefully kept her baby at a safe distance from the hole through which the monkey's hand was continually intruding. At length the hour of revenge arrived. The little monkey had by this time been allowed to go about by itself, and unfortunately it passed near the knot hole. In a moment the big monkey's hand was darted through, and as quickly withdrawn, bringing with it the tail of the little one. He then fixed his foot firmly on one side of the knot hole, and tugged away with all his might at the little fellow's tail. The poor baby monkey, on being treated so rudely and unexpectedly, set up a heart-rending cry. The mother rushed to its assistance, and, seeing her child fastened as it were to the wall, seized it by the arms and pulled with all her might to release it. One may imagine the screaming and the noise that resulted, and which speedily brought to the spot the keeper, at the sight of whose whip the jealous monkey at once released the baby's tail, and crouched in the farthest corner of his cage.

The Monkey and the Dog

ONCE upon a time two Italian boys were the possessors of a hand organ and a monkey. The monkey was very clever, and never failed to draw large crowds of onlookers. One day, while it was showing off its tricks, a dog jumped at it a number of times, and worried it very sadly. The Italian boys, of course, greatly disliked the dog's naughty manners, and it was agreed between them and the master of the dog that the monkey and the dog should fight it out alone. The monkey, as he was the smaller of the two animals, was to be armed with a stick.

A woolly saki monkey from the Amazon River. Its hair is extremely soft and light, and is ruffled by the merest breeze. What a queer-looking animal!

A stick was brought, and then the monkey had to be taught quickly the part he was to act. One of the Italian boys went on all fours, barking like a dog, while the other boy got on his back, grasped his hair, and appeared to beat him about the head with a stick. The monkey looked on with seriousness, and when the lesson was over took the stick with the air of a man who knew his work and meant to do it.

A ring having been formed, the dog and the monkey were placed within it. The dog flew at the monkey with open mouth, but the monkey, leaping to one side, jumped to the dog's back, took hold of his ear, and began hitting away at his head with the stick; and within a short time the dog was willing to acknowledge the monkey as conqueror.

The gelada baboon comes from Africa. A flowing mantle of brown hair falls from the shoulders. Its tail is like that of a lion, and its disposition is quite like one too.

The Monkey and the Pitcher Plant

WHILE two Englishmen, brothers, were traveling through the island of Ceylon, one of them stopped and, looking anxiously around, said, "I surely heard a cry as if some one was hurt." The brothers followed the sound, which came from a group of coconut trees. Suddenly one of them called out, "Here it is, Arthur!" and pointed to a monkey that was lying on the ground, suffering from a severe wound.

They carefully bound up the injured limb and took the monkey with them, agreeing that they would not part with their patient until he was quite cured and able to return to the forest.

They traveled for two days, and were still about sixty miles from the city to which they were going. The heat was very oppressive. Water became scarcer as they continued their trip, and the men began to suffer of extreme thirst. When they were still thirty miles from their destination, they sat down at the foot of a palm tree, quite exhausted, and wondered if they would have to perish there for the lack of water.

Just then the monkey, which had been resting beside them, rose up and went eagerly forward as if in search of something valuable. Watching his movements, the brothers summoned their fast-waning strength, and slowly followed him. They soon discovered that he had found the object of his search, which was the "monkey-cup," as it is called, from its being sought after by these animals; more commonly it is known by the name of "pitcher plant."

The leaves of this plant are formed into natural pitchers holding sometimes as much as a pint or more of water. Each pitcher has a lid that opens when the weather is moist, and shuts quite close when it is dry. A hook grows beneath the lid of each pitcher, by which it is held to a branch for support. The water that is found in these pitchers is pure.

With this water the brothers relieved their thirst, and then joyfully went on their way with their little companion, now an object of the greatest interest to them. When they reached their friends, they said: "This monkey was the means of saving our lives! He showed us where to find water."

A young howling monkey from South America. A curious "sound box" in the throat enables the howling monkey to utter long, deep roars. Between three and five years of age, it develops a heavy beard.

Monkeys at a Gospel Service

ONCE a missionary in Africa was holding a service with some of the native people in a yard surrounded by a board fence, and close to a large grove. As usual, the meeting opened with singing.

Some monkeys that were scampering around in the trees near by were attracted by the music, and decided to go nearer. So along they came,—old monkeys, baby monkeys, and all. They climbed up on the fence surrounding the place of meeting, and sat there listening to the music. When the missionary began to speak, they still sat there, seemingly listening with as much interest as ever. Once in a while one of the baby monkeys would get a little restless, and begin to move about. Then the mother monkey would give him a few smart taps on the side of the head, which would make him sit quiet again. The monkeys sat there quietly through the whole sermon. After the last song had been sung and the people began to go away, the monkeys climbed down from the fence and went back to the grove, seeming to have enjoyed the meeting as well as the natives did.

A Rat for a Cushion

IN ONE of the zoölogical gardens in Europe a cage of large white rats stood near a cage of monkeys. The monkeys had always shown so much curiosity about the rats that the keeper decided to put one of the rats in with them to see what they would do.

They screamed with delight when the rat entered, and began to make friends with him. The rat was inclined to run away from them for the first day or two; but, seeing that they did not intend to do him any harm, he lost his fear, and permitted the monkeys to fondle and caress him as much as they liked. This they did constantly, stroking his white fur, holding him in their arms, and offering him part of their food. They even picked out choice morsels and gave them to the rat.

One day a new idea occurred to the oldest monkey. He had the rat in his arms; and, putting him gently on the floor of the cage, he *very cautiously* sat on him! Here was a new way to use a friend. The rat did not move, nor did he seem to object to the queer use to which the monkey was putting him. As for the monkey, he looked about with a broad grin on his face, and chattered with delight over the soft cushion he had found.

After sitting there for a while, he got up so the other monkeys might try his cushion, and they were all as pleased as he had been. From that time on the rat was in daily use as a cushion, and he took his part with very good temper, never objecting to it in the least.

MONKEYS CAN UNDERSTAND MUSICAL SOUNDS

Professor Garner tells of watching some little capuchin monkeys in the London Zoo when a violin was being played. He says these pretty little creatures have very expressive faces, and the changes in their faces and voices while listening to the music were very rapid. The three in the first cage at once rushed up to their box, and then all peeped out excited and chattering. One by one they came down and listened to the music with intense curiosity, shrieking and making faces at a crescendo, shaking the wires angrily at a discord, and putting their heads almost upside down at low and musical passages.

This strange-looking specimen was a gift from a prince of India to Mussolini of Italy

The Monkey That Scared a Mother

MANY years ago a vessel sailed from Jamaica to England, and among the passengers was the mother of an infant only a few weeks old. The voyage was very pleasant, the weather remarkably fine, and the passengers did their best to make the time pass agreeably.

One beautiful afternoon the captain saw a distant sail — a sight that is always welcome at sea. The discovery attracted the attention of all on board; and, after the captain had gratified his own curiosity, he politely offered his field glass to the baby's mother, that she might have a clearer view of the distant vessel.

At that moment she had the little baby in her arms; so, wrapping a shawl about it, she placed it on a deck chair on which she had been sitting. The captain helped her to set the glass, but scarcely had she applied her eye to it when a sailor called out, "The monkey has the baby!" The mother's feelings may be imagined when, on quickly turning round, she saw that a large and active monkey that was on board the vessel had grasped her baby firmly with one arm, and with the other was nimbly climbing the masts, with the evident intention of reaching the very top of the mainmast.

The mother, at the sight of her baby's being taken from her, fainted. The captain was at his wit's end. He was afraid that if he sent a sailor to climb up to the monkey, it would drop the child and endeavor to escape by leaping from one mast to another. In the meantime he heard the infant cry, and thought that the monkey was holding it too tight. But he saw the monkey imitating the motions of a nurse, soothing and caressing the child, and even trying to hush it to sleep.

Several plans were tried to bring the monkey down from his lofty seat, but all in vain. At length the captain ordered every man to conceal himself below deck. The order was promptly obeyed, and the captain took a seat where he could see without being seen. To his great relief, the monkey, on finding the deck clear, cautiously descended from the masthead and replaced the infant on the deck chair from which it had been taken. The poor little baby was cold and fretful, and no doubt frightened, but was in every other respect free from injury.

No doubt this mischievous monkey was tied up or put into a cage after this experience.

A South African Monkey

OVER in South Africa lives a small gray monkey named Jennie. She has a little square house on top of a smooth pole eight feet high, and she is fastened to this pole with a chain and a large wire ring that slides up or down as Jennie climbs up or down the pole. Jennie feels quite safe and happy in her little house up in the air, as the dogs in the neighborhood can not bother her when she is in it.

When given some food she is especially fond of, she will often climb the pole and sit on top of her house to eat it. She is very fond of tomatoes, and she likes potatoes, carrots, and corn; but she is especially happy when given a banana or some peanuts. She will make a thorough search of every pocket, in the hope of finding a nut. Jennie, like most children, has a sweet tooth, and she is quite contented if chewing a piece of sugar cane.

When she is chained to a tree in the yard, she has a good time. It is very interesting to watch her jump from limb to limb, sometimes hanging by her front or back feet.

She is very fond of children, and gets very angry if she thinks a child is in trouble. Often when she hears them scream, even in play, she thinks they are hurt, and she will try to reach the offender, making ugly faces at him all the while. One time a mother had to spank her little boy out in the yard, and it made Jennie very angry. For a long time afterwards she would throw small sticks and stones at the woman whenever she came near.

The children often go for a long walk and take Jennie along. When she gets tired of walking, she will jump up on the shoulder of one of the children and ride until she is rested and ready to run again. If one goes out at night when Jennie is asleep in her little house at the top of the pole, he will see her long tail hanging out of the small door of the house. Her tail is nearly two feet long, and she has a hard time twisting around just right to get all of it in the house. She doesn't seem to care much whether it hangs out or not, except when rain is falling.

Here is Borneo, pet orang-utan of the Minneapolis Zoo, riding on his tricycle.

LOS ANGELES MONKEY FARM

This chimpanzee is devoted to his pony, and they have great fun together.

A powerful Japanese monkey that lives in the cooler parts of Japan.
He does not object to the snow and ice in winter. His face
is the color of red brick.

The Monkey That Saved a Boy

GO AWAY, Maimu, I'm tired of you! Go!" Cyril threw a stone; the little black-faced monkey cried out sharply, swung himself into a tree, and rocked to and fro, nursing his hurt foot. Cyril then fed the swans; but he could not feel happy, for he knew he had been unkind.

"I'm going down by the road, mother," he called out as he ran toward the gate.

Some camels were passing; behind was an Arab woman, riding a donkey. Cyril crossed the road to get a better view of them, for he had been in Egypt only a short time, and there was much he had not seen yet. The boy strolled along behind the animals, and soon found himself by the canal banks, where he stopped to watch the dark gray buffaloes in the water.

A large flat-bottomed boat came toward him. A tall Arab, in a loose white robe, was guiding with a long pole, while his son stood at the other end. When opposite Cyril, the boy put out his hand and asked for a coin. Cyril tossed a pebble, which the boy caught cleverly, laughed when he saw it was not a coin, and threw it back. Both enjoyed the game, and kept it up for some minutes. The boat came very close to the bank, and the pebble was tossed from one to the other by little jerks of the hand.

All at once, Cyril felt himself being seized and lifted into the boat. "I don't want a trip; I must get home," he cried. For answer the boatman pushed into the middle of the canal. Cyril was a good swimmer. Certain that the Arab meant to steal him, he made up his mind to dash for freedom. He sprang overboard, but was at once dragged back, had a cloth forced into his mouth, and cords bound tightly around his wrists and ankles.

It grew very dark. Cyril's bonds hurt him; he felt

The common monkey of India

very helpless, and feared he would never see his mother again. At last the boat stopped, and he was lifted out and dragged past some palm trees into a dirty tent. A camel was resting near the opening. An Arab woman just outside was cooking over a fire. The grain was soon crisp and brown. The cord around Cyril's hands was loosened, and he was very glad to be given some of the pods to eat. In a few minutes, however, he was again bound. In pain and fear he tossed in the darkness while the others slept.

Suddenly a warm touch on his face startled him. Had the Arab come to kill him? Something moved near his wrist, and he fancied he heard a faint grinding sound. Then he found his hands were free, and that some one was working at the other cord. Could it be a friend?

Very carefully he passed his hand down, expecting to find it was the little Arab boy. But no! Something warm and furry was there. Before he could think what it might be, the second cord was loose. Scarcely daring to breathe, he crawled past the Arabs, and lifted the flap of the tent door just enough to let himself through.

A chilly morning at the zoo

The light was very faint, but Cyril was glad indeed to see it. There was no sound but the waving of the palm branches overhead. "I am free," he thought, and started to run, when, at that moment, his leg was caught from behind. In terror, he turned round. Then he forgot all else while he hugged Maimu closely, crying out: "Maimu, Maimu, you have come after me and saved me, and I was so cruel to you! What a brick you are!" But Maimu scrambled out of his arms, tugged at him to go on, and Cyril, remembering his danger, ran quickly.

Once he glanced back, caught a glimpse of a tall figure, and rushed on wildly. A stone hit his leg. He rolled and fell into a hole. Covering himself with the sand, he lay there until he felt he could scarcely breathe. He was terribly afraid the Arab was standing above him; but, in spite of the feeling, he shook the sand off his face, opened his eyes, and looked around. No one was there. He drew himself up and peeped.

He saw the Arab a little way off, climbing up a date palm. At first Cyril was puzzled; then he understood. The dark object above the clusters in the palm was Maimu, but the Arab thought it was he. Cyril seized his chance when the man's back was turned, and crept out of the hole. He raced along, at times almost choking with fear that he was going the wrong way, and would find himself back at the tent. The palm trees seemed endless. Utterly spent, he at last caught the flash of the city carriage lamps, staggered forward into the road, fell down, and knew no more. Friendly hands carried the boy to the hotel where his parents were staying.

. . . . .

Two months later Cyril sailed for England, taking with him his good friend Maimu, the black-faced monkey that had followed him at a distance that eventful afternoon to return good for evil.

A black spider monkey from the Panama country

How Monkeys Help One Another

WO boys were once given an unusual entertainment, and taught a splendid lesson too, by a troop of ring-tailed monkeys that wanted to cross a stream of water that they could not leap. Many monkeys, you know, hate to get into water. When the boys, who were with an army officer, heard the chattering of the approaching troop, they concealed themselves in a spot where the movements of the monkeys could be plainly seen, for they knew something interesting would happen.

Presently the troop appeared on the opposite bank of the stream, headed by an old gray chief, and officered like so many soldiers. One of them ran out upon a projecting rock; and, after looking across the stream, as if calculating the distance, scampered back, and appeared to communicate with the chief.

Then began a movement in the troop. Soon they all collected around a tall tree that grew over the narrowest part of the stream, and twenty or thirty of them scampered up its trunk. On reaching a high point, the foremost, a strong fellow, ran out upon a limb, and, taking two or three turns of his tail around it, slipped off, and hung head downward.

The next on the limb, also a stout monkey, climbed down the body of the first; and, wrapping his tail tightly around the neck and forearm of the strong fellow, dropped off with his head downward. The others repeated this process, until the last on the string rested his forepaws on the ground. The living chain now began swinging backward and forward like the pendulum of a clock. This continued until the monkey at the end of the chain was thrown to a strong branch of a tree on the opposite bank. Here, after two or three vibrations, he clutched a limb, and held fast.

The chain was now fast at both ends, forming a complete suspension bridge, over which the whole troop, to the number of four or five hundred, passed with great rapidity. The troop was now on the other side; but how were the animals forming the bridge to get themselves over? The boys were much excited to see how it would be done.

The end on the other side was much lower down, and number one on this side, with a half dozen of his neighbors, would, it seemed, be dashed against the opposite bank or soused into the water. A monkey was now seen to attach his tail to the tail of the lowest monkey on the bridge, another girdled him in a similar manner, and

So far as monkeys go, this orang-utan is a fine-looking specimen. He stands at the head of the apes. His movements are quick and powerful. And with a sort of lingo known to his tribe, he can doubtless deliver a pleasing oration to an assembly of apes.

The chimpanzee is generally considered the most intelligent of all the monkey tribes. It is the chimpanzee that is usually trained to do "stunts" in the menageries.

another, and so on, until a dozen more were, added to the string.

These last monkeys were all powerful fellows; and, running up to a high limb, they lifted the bridge into a horizontal position. Then a scream from the last monkey of the new formation warned the tail end that all was ready; the next moment the whole chain was swung over and landed safely on the opposite bank. The lowermost links now dropped off like a melting candle, while the higher ones leaped to the branches, and came down the trunk. The whole troop then scampered off into the forest, and disappeared.

The boys were thus reminded of how much may be done through united effort and brotherly kindness.

Another howling monkey from South America. Its remarkable tail, used as a fifth hand, is also very useful as a prop, enabling him to stand erect.

Monkeys That Pick Coconuts

THE Malays catch certain monkeys in traps while they are still very young. There is a particular species of them that they must get for coconut picking called the pig-tailed rhesus, because it is one of the strongest kinds, and obeys the men.

These monkeys have each a pouch in the neck; and, when they are fed, they push the food through into these pouches, which open on each side into the mouth. When the pouches are full, the little fellows will go off and sit down to chew their food thoroughly before they swallow it.

Of course, they can't wear collars; so the master puts a small belt around the waist of his monkey, and fastens a chain to this belt. He then ties a long rope to the end of the chain, and sends the monkey up the tree after the nuts.

But you wonder how he teaches it to pick the coconuts. First he drives a stake in the ground, and puts an old nut on it. (The squirrels there cut a round hole through the hard husk and shell with their teeth, and eat out the white meat. Then these nuts drop off, and are useful in teaching the monkeys.) The man ties his little pupil near, and spins the nut, pushing it off the stick. After a while the monkey imitates him, and pushes the nut off too.

Have you all seen coconuts in the stores? Well, they have husks on when picked, and are about as large as a small round watermelon.

The master walks up to a coconut tree, and points to the nuts, saying, *"Naik."* At first the monkey does not want to climb; so the man gets a red pepper, and rubs the ends of a broken piece in the eyes of the poor little fellow. It jumps up, and begins climbing as fast as it can, to get away from the cruel man.

He keeps urging it on by saying, *"Naik."* At last it reaches the top, and rests on the stems of the palms, watching the man to see what he will do next. It sees the cluster of big nuts; and as soon as the man says, *"Yo,"* and jerks the rope, the monkey starts twisting the nut with one of its hands and the opposite foot. Soon the short stem breaks; and down comes the nut, the little picker hanging on to the tree by the free hand and foot.

After picking all the ripe ones and a few green ones for us to eat, it follows its chain back, and slides down the tree. The master receives about two cents, or the value of a coconut, for each tree his little servant picks. The trees are very high, and the monkeys climb about twenty-five in a day. All they get is their rice and fruit.

IMITATORS

A traveler in South America tells of an interesting thing he saw in monkey life when his boat stopped for a week at a certain village on one of the branches of the great Amazon.

He was in the habit of rising early and washing himself and brushing his teeth on deck, dipping his sponge and toothbrush, of course, in water. He had pursued this practice for some days, when, to his surprise, he noticed a monkey engaged in the same operation. Other monkeys were watching, and, after a few mornings, dozens of them were to be seen along the shore, washing themselves, or cleaning their teeth with small sticks of willow!

MONKEY HAIRS

Many of the heathen Chinese have considerable respect for the monkey. A missionary to China tells of his children's having to watch their pet monkey rather closely, for if they did not, the monkey would soon have no hair! Where do you suppose his hair would go? When a boy baby is born, many Chinese think that if only they can obtain a few monkey hairs to put in his first bath water, these will insure the child a good start in life. If they cannot get any hairs from the monkey, they will give it some food, like a sweet potato, and then pick up any bits of peeling he might leave and place these in the baby's bath water. Of course, when these people adopt the principles of Christianity they forget all such silly notions.

A pair of pretty marmosets. In its fondness for insects, a marmoset has been seen to tear the pictures of insects out of a book and eat them.

The Marmosets

WHAT curious little animals these are, with bodies covered with soft fur like a squirrel's, and faces like a monkey's. When full grown, they are only about seven or eight inches long besides the tail, which measures about a foot.

They live in the warm climate of South America, and are very sensitive to the cold. There, in the mighty forests, where the trees are so lofty that no man can climb them, so dense that there is a kind of upper story on the interlaced tops where many birds and animals live without descending to earth, where there is neither summer nor winter, but only the changes from hour to hour of the equatorial day, the beautiful little marmosets, whose fur looks like the plumage of birds, and whose twittering voices imitate the notes of birds, live and have their being.

The marmoset is a very agile little animal when in good health, leaping like a squirrel from place to place. If alarmed or irritated, it gives a sharp little whistle. Its diet consists largely of insects, eggs, and fruits.

Merchants who do business with Brazil often import marmosets for pets. At first they are very shy, but they soon become playful and affectionate. In cold weather they like to curl up in a pile of bedding or warm clothes.

When properly tamed, the marmoset will come and sit on its owner's hand, its little paws clinging tightly to his fingers, and its tail coiled over his hand or wrist. Or it will clamber up his arm and sit on his shoulder; or, if very cold, hide itself beneath his coat or even creep into a convenient pocket.

MORE MONKEY FACTS

Monkeys know enough to learn by experience. They handle very carefully a tool that has once cut them.

A monkey that had at times received bits of sugar wrapped in pieces of paper was once offered a little package containing a wasp. When he unfolded the paper, the wasp stung him. After that, before opening a package he held it to his ear.

Some monkeys, especially baboons, throw sticks and stones at their enemies. Monkeys quickly learn the uses of screws, keys, and hammers.

In India, some monkeys are taught to work a large fan hung from the ceiling of a room. In Africa, baboons are taught to guard their masters' property, to drive oxen, and to blow the bellows for the blacksmith. Young orang-utans have been taught to use a cup and spoon, and to make a bed.

Chimpanzees are very sportive in their wild state. They use a hollow tree for a drum to call the little ones to play; and when the youngsters are gathered, the old ones sit around and watch them, correcting them if they do anything wrong.

A kind of Gibbon monkey, called the "woo-woo," is the only brute that can sing. It runs through the semitones of the octave with much accuracy.

Many monkeys will fold the sick in their arms, will soothe their companions when injured.

Mother monkeys have been seen to wash the faces of their children in a stream. Some monkeys have died of grief over the loss of their babies. Some of them adopt and care for orphan monkeys.